KU-369-625

B

A PICK-YOUR-PATH
ADVENTURE

Ring Bearer
A Pick Your Path Adventure
by Dan Metcalf
Illustrated by Maurizio Campidelli

Published by Ransom Publishing Ltd.
Unit 7, Brocklands Farm, West Meon, Hampshire
GU32 1JN, UK
www.ransom.co.uk

ISBN   978 178591 792 9
First published in 2019

DAN METCALF

ILLUSTRATED BY
MAURIZIO CAMPIDELLI

Ransom

AUTHOR'S NOTE

If, like me, you love games and adventure, then you're in for a real treat.

Game books like this one are what made me fall in love with reading.

In fact, this isn't really a book at all; it's a fully interactive adventure that will have you guessing and guessing.

What happens next? You decide!

HOW IT WORKS

Start off with the introduction. That gives you two options. You can either pick an option OR you can just be random and flip a coin!

Go to the option you want, then carry on reading!

If you choose to flip a coin ...

this is **HEADS**

and this is **TAILS**.

INTRODUCTION

Shoeless and dressed in simple peasant clothes, you walk along a country path. You have walked far and, tired and weary, you lean heavily on your staff.

You are The Chosen One. You wear the Ring of the Fallen, a sacred, magic relic that can unite the scattered kingdoms. It was never a quest you asked for, but you accept the responsibility and now you travel the lands as a healer. Recently you have heard of a hooded stranger making trouble and asking questions about you.

Your country path splits into two, next to a signpost. **EAST: City of Light. WEST: City of Darkness.**

Make your choice now. Pick your path!

EAST » 24

WEST » 15

You hand over the ring.

'Very good. A wise choice,' says the hooded stranger, as he puts it on. He moves to the door of the hovel and opens it. Skeletal wraiths pour in, their bloodshot eyes staring, and head towards you, ready to suck out your life and soul.

'Akarasta!' chants the stranger, and the wraiths evaporate into the air. Within moments, they are all gone.

'You wanted to do good?' you ask.

'Of course,' says the stranger. 'Just because I look like the bad guy ... '

YOU WIN A POWERFUL ALLY

TRY AGAIN?

2

You strike first. The ring emits a powerful blast that knocks down the stranger. As he lies on the ground, you approach carefully, feeling uneasy. Something bad is afoot.

The hooded stranger rises and pulls back his hood to reveal a familiar face: yours! He is a stranger no longer. 'H-how?' you stutter.

You see your own face smile back at you. But this face is older, scarred and weathered. 'You must finish me. It is my fate,' the stranger says. 'Do it now.'

You reluctantly kill your future self.

YOU WON ... I THINK!

TRY AGAIN?

You are alone in the city again. It seems
deserted; litter is strewn across the
streets and there is an eerie silence.
Then you hear a sound.

The town hall clock strikes 13 and
wraiths appear out of the ground,
wailing and grabbing at your legs. Their
lifeless bodies are translucent, their skin
is falling from their faces and their eyes
look sad and desperate.

One catches you with its skeletal claw.

What do you do?

RUN » 9

FIGHT » 23

4

You are surrounded in the marketplace. You struggle to think. What can you do?

With a smile, the witch waves her hand — and the crowd's eyes all turn yellow. 'Kill! Kill! Kill!' they chant.

'They are all my slaves now,' the witch tells you.

With your ringed fist, you punch the air. A shockwave rocks the city and the pure white beam of light streaming from your fist knocks the crowd unconscious.

'I'm sorry,' you say. You run. Your time in this city is over, but perhaps you may be welcome in another place.

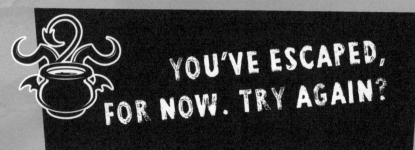

YOU'VE ESCAPED, FOR NOW. TRY AGAIN?

5

You win the bet.

'Huh! Typical!' says the disgruntled owner. He takes your order and comes back minutes later with huge, strangely green-looking pie on a plate. Then you notice a nasty wound on his arm.

'Where did you get that?' you ask.

The café owner shrugs. 'A hooded stranger came in asking about you, Ring Bearer. He grabbed me and left this mark,' he says, rubbing the wound. 'But now you're here with your magic ring, you can heal me.'

Will you heal his arm?

YES » 19

NO » 14

Wary, the café owner refuses. You smile, holding the orb in your hand, as he pulls out a club from under the counter. The end of the club is packed with metal spikes. 'Are you the Ring Bearer that the stranger ordered me to kill?'

Without thinking, you say, 'No'.

'Oops!' says the café owner. 'Poisoned by your own chalice, eh, Ring Bearer?'

You look down and the orb you are holding glows red and bursts into flames. The flames consume you too, and you scream and fall to the floor. The magic flame destroys both you and the ring.

BAD LUCK!

TRY AGAIN?

7

'I can't, I must go — Ow!'

The woman hits you from behind with a large talisman. Everything turns to black.

When you come around, you are tied up on a chair. The hooded stranger is standing in front of you.

'Greetings, Ring Bearer. I have waited a long time to meet you,' he says. 'Now, give me the ring.'

GIVE IT » 1

REFUSE » 25

The young woman leads you down a secluded alleyway.

'Why must I hide? Has the hooded stranger been poking around?' you ask her. A cold shiver runs down your spine. A bad feeling. You should never have chosen this path.

The woman faces you, her yellow eyes glowing. She has a witch's power.

She looks deep into you, tasting your soul. 'The stranger offered riches. He said to bring the Ring Bearer — dead or alive.'

What do you do?

RUN » 12

FIGHT » 20

9

You run to a diner, where you are the only customer.

'Escaping the wraiths, eh?' says the waitress with a friendly smile.

'What are they? Those ... things?' you ask. You gratefully take a glass of something and drink it down in one go.

'The wraiths? They're the souls of the damned, trapped and hungry for blood. We've been plagued by them for years.'

She sees your ring and gasps. 'It's you! The Ring Bearer! Everyone's been talking about you. You have the power to rid us of those beasts! Will you help?'

YES » 23

NO » 10

You shake your head.

'I ... I cannot help you. I'm sorry,' you say. Your face reddens with shame. The waitress flounces away, disappointed in you.

There is a banging on the door.

The waitress opens it and is pulled outside by a skeletal hand.

You turn as she screams and the wraiths enter. The wraiths grab your hand and steal the ring, then pull off your limbs, one by one ...

OUCH! YOU LOSE

TRY AGAIN?

11

'You're going to kill me?' croaks the witch.

'You give me no choice,' you say. 'The ring must be kept safe.'

The witch smiles. 'The only way to safety is not by running away, but by confronting the hooded stranger. He waits for you in the City of Darkness,' she says.

You use the ring to kill her painlessly, whispering an ancient spell that lets her fall into a deep slumber.

Which city will you go to now?

DARKNESS » 15

LIGHT » 17

12

You start to run, but she gives chase.

'STOP, THIEF!' she yells, and the market-goers all turn to look at you. Their faces turn dark, but you keep running. Now every burly market stall-holder is after you, trying to grab you or trip you.

Finally a large man, muscled and bald, dives on you and tackles you to the floor. 'We have you now, Ring Bearer!'

What are you going to do? The ring has powers, but should you use them? Or should you simply give in?

USE THE RING » 4

GIVE IN » 26

The coin falls: it is tails. 'I hate to go back on a deal,' you say, 'but the ring is not mine to give.'

'You cheat!' the man shouts.

'Wait! Maybe there is something I can interest you in … ' You rub the ring and it produces a small ball of lightning which shimmers in front of you.

'What is it?' asks the man, now curious.

'It's a charm. You may have it; the honest man will take this and ascend to greatness. The dishonest man will perish.

Does he take it or refuse it?'

TAKE IT » 21

REFUSE IT » 6

14

'I cannot use my powers on such a small wound,' you say. 'I'm sorry. You will have to use traditional herbs and a bandage.'

The café owner grunts, disappointed. He moves to the back of the café and returns with a spiked club.

'Ha! The Ring Bearer must die!' he screams, swinging his weapon.

You dodge him and strike back with the full power of the ring. He falls down, crumbling to dust.

You look around the café and run. Your time here is over.

GOOD JOB, KILLER!

TRY AGAIN?

The City of Darkness is covered in shadow, true to its name.

As you walk around the streets, dark figures run past and dart into doorways. You manage to stop one.

'Excuse me, where can I find lodgings?' The young woman has fear etched on her face.

'Come with me. Quick!'

Do you follow her?

YES » 22

NO » 3

16

You tell her you will stay, just as the door to her home smashes into pieces.

'Stand back,' you yell to her, as an army of skeletal wraiths rushes inside. You turn over a table and use it as protection. Rubbing the ring, you fire blasts of power from it. You hit each wraith in turn, and they scream, falling to the ground and crumbing to dust.

'You are a hero!' says the young woman.

You are given the key to the city and you live there happily for the rest of your life — as the city's guide and protector.

AH, A HAPPY ENDING!

TRY AGAIN?

17

Wandering the alleyways of the City of Light, you find yourself in need of food.

You enter a café and the owner welcomes you.

'Greetings!' says the owner. You start to take out your purse of coins, but he stops you. 'Put that away! This is a unique café. I spin a coin, and if it is heads, you eat for free. If it is tails, you lose, and I take that pretty ring of yours.'

'You can't be serious?' you say.

He nods, deadly serious.

Hungry, you take the bet.

HEADS » 5

TAILS » 13

You slam your staff down, but it has little effect. You shake it, but no power radiates from it.

'Pity,' says the hooded stranger. 'I had been looking forward to a good fight.'

The hooded stranger casts a hex which raises you high in the air, then lets you fall. As you lie on the ground, winded and unable to move, the stranger comes close.

'I'll take that ... '

The ring slips from your finger, as your vision fades to black.

OOPS. YOU LOSE
TRY AGAIN?

19

You lay your hands on the wound and the ring glows. Smoke rises from the café owner's arm and, when you release your grip, the wound has healed.

'Blow me down!' says the owner. 'The hooded stranger said you'd fall for it!'

Confused, you look at your hands. It was a trick! A magical black rash has formed over your hands and arms. It quickly spreads. Within the hour, you are dead.

The café owner takes the ring from your dead hand and sends a raven to fetch the hooded stranger.

You have failed in your quest.

DRAT!

PLAY AGAIN?

The witch reaches out to grab you, but you use your staff to knock her legs from under her.

She falls to the floor, but still has some fight left in her.

She fires a bolt of energy from her eyes, straight at you.

You deflect it, using a mirror on the staff to blast it back at her.

Now she's weak.

Do you kill her or walk away?

KILL HER » 11

WALK AWAY » 4

21

Entranced, the café owner reaches out and takes the orb of light.

'So this will bring me power and greatness?' he asks.

'We'll soon see,' you say.

The orb begins to flash and flicker. Your smile fades.

The light grows in his hand until it is so large it bursts into flame.

The fire spreads until it consumes the entire café, destroying everyone in it, including you.

PLAYER PERISHED.

PITY! TRY AGAIN?

The young woman pulls you into her home, a hovel filled with talismans. They are meant to ward off evil spirits. There is one from every religion known to you.

'You're afraid. Of what?' you ask.

'Take your pick: wraiths, thieves, the hooded stranger ... '

She glances at your ring. 'The hooded stranger will be after you!' she says. 'Stay here! Protect me! Please!'

Do you agree?

YES » 16

NO » 7

23

You leave the café and walk out into the street. Turning slowly, you slam your staff on the ground. It fires a bright light in all directions, vapourising the wraiths in seconds.

'Very clever, Ring Bearer.' The voice has come from behind you. You turn to see the hooded stranger who has been asking about you.

'What do you want?' you ask.

'To fight, of course — to the death!'

You see no other option. This will solve things, once and for all, you think. Which weapon do you choose?

STAFF » 18

RING » 2

24

Your path to the east takes you to the City of Light, famed for its jewelled spires. You wander around its streets for a while, gazing at the beautiful structures.

You enter the marketplace and lower your hood, showing your face.

The crowd begins to whisper. A young woman approaches.

'Is it you, Ring Bearer?' You nod. 'Then you cannot be here. Follow me.'

Do you go with her?

YES » 8

NO » 17

'Never!' you yell.

'Very well,' says the hooded stranger. 'Then we must fight.'

Your bindings fall away and the stranger fires a magical blast straight at you — which you block with your ring.

You fight back, firing energy bolts, but the stranger is stronger. His magical blasts keep coming, hitting you with incantations until you are lying on the floor, breathless and close to death.

The stranger reaches down and takes your ring from you, as you breathe your last breath ...

GOOD EFFORT, BUT YOU LOSE. TRY AGAIN?

26

Using the ring's powers could hurt people, so you don't use it.

You hold up your hands and the witch binds them, leading you back down the alley.

'Wise choice,' she says.

'So which will it be? Will you take me to the stranger dead — or alive?' you ask.

'I think you know, Ring Bearer ... '

A flash of a sword is the last thing you see ...

OOPS! DEAD AGAIN!

RESTART?

THANKS FOR PLAYING

There are lots of ways
your story can turn out.

Why not try again and
pick a different path?

HAVE YOU PICKED YOUR PATH
THROUGH THESE?

MOON
UNIT

DAN METCALF

ZOMBIE
STORM

DAN METCALF

ABOUT THE AUTHOR

Born at an early age, Dan Metcalf always loved writing and was the kid who would stay in at breaktime at school ON PURPOSE to finish the story he was writing.

Dan is now a professional daydreamer and full-time writer, He thinks that many book people are a bit sniffy about games, and says he wrote PICK YOUR PATH to teach them a lesson!